Everyday Mathematics®

MINUTE MATH® KINDERGARTEN

The University of Chicago School Mathematics Project

Wright Group

The McGraw·Hill Companies

www.WrightGroup.com

Printed in the United States of America.

Send all inquiries to:
Wright Group/McGraw-Hill
P.O. Box 812960
Chicago, IL 60681

ISBN 0-07-604511-0
       7 8 9 CPS 12 11 10 09 08 07

The McGraw·Hill Companies

Authors

Jean Bell
Max Bell
Dorothy Freedman
Nancy Goodsell (First Edition)
Nancy Hanvey
Kate Morrison

Contributors

Mary Fullmer
Rosalie Fruchter
Curtis Lieneck

Introduction

Kindergarten Minute Math® is an important part of the *Kindergarten Everyday Mathematics*® program. It reinforces the activities in the *Teacher's Guide to Activities*™, with special emphasis on developing problem-solving and mental mathematics skills. Plan to use this book regularly. Since *Minute Math* activities are short and require no materials, they are easy to fit in during the day (meetings, lining up, gathering for group time, waiting times, and so on). You might hang your *Minute Math* book on a hook in your classroom meeting area or near the doorway so you can find it easily when the opportunity for a quick activity presents itself. Some teachers even carry the book in their pocket so it will always be available!

Although the book is divided into the following three parts, any activity can be used with appropriate changes and recycled often during the year. We also encourage you and your class to invent your own *Minute Math* activities.

Part 1: Pages 5–66 support the Ongoing Daily Routines and Sections 1 and 2 in the *Teacher's Guide to Activities*.

Part 2: Pages 67–196 support the Ongoing Daily Routines and Sections 3 through 6 in the *Teacher's Guide to Activities*.

Part 3: Pages 197–258 support the Ongoing Daily Routines and Sections 7 and 8 in the *Teacher's Guide to Activities*.

Part 1

The activities in Part 1 reinforce the Ongoing Daily Routines and the activities through Section 2 in the *Teacher's Guide to Activities*. Remember that any *Minute Math* activity can be varied and used as often as you like throughout the year.

NOTES

Introduction to Counting
Counting

Always be on the lookout for opportunities to ask questions that require counting, such as:

How many students are here today?
How many students are having hot lunch?
How many students brought their own lunch?

Finger Talk
Counting

Can fingers talk? Can you use 1 finger to say "Shhhh"? (Hold 1 finger to lips; children copy.)

Can you use 2 fingers to say "Think hard"? (Tap forehead with 2 fingers.)

Can you use 3 fingers to say "Oops! I said that wrong"? (Cover lips with 3 fingers.)

Can you use 4 fingers to say "Goodbye"? (Waggle 4 fingers.)

What can you use 5 fingers for?

Let's Count to 10
Counting

Let's count to 10 starting with 1.

Let's start with 3 and count on to 8.

Now let's start with 2 and count on to 9.

Counting to 10
Counting

How many children can count to 10?

Call on individual volunteers to count out loud to 10. Then have the class count to 10 in unison.

Introduction to Number Stories
Number Stories

The children will find number stories more interesting if you use their names and situations with which they are familiar. (James, Rita, and Marcus were having a snack. How many kids were at the snack table?)

Encourage children to get in the habit of telling number stories by using numbers and naming the objects being counted. (3 cats, 5 cookies, and so on.)

Whenever possible, have children act out number stories they have difficulty understanding. Later in the year, if a chalkboard is nearby, use diagrams or number sentences to keep track of the action.

Outdoor Fun
Number Stories

A crow, a robin, a blue jay, and a cardinal were sitting on a fence. How many birds were sitting on the fence? (4 birds)

Bridget was hunting for treasures on the beach. She found a shell, a feather, and a stone. How many things did Bridget find? (3 things)

Kathleen, the twins, and Leo were having a picnic. How many children were having a picnic? (4 children)

What Numbers Have You Seen?
Numeration

From the time you woke up this morning until now, what numbers have you seen?

When have you used numbers today? (Counting snacks, looking at the clock or calendar, seeing the room number, and so on)

Did I Do It Right?
Counting

I'm going to count to 5: 1, 2, 3, 4, 6, 5. Did I do it right? (no) What did I do wrong? (Switched 6 and 5)

How would you count to 5? (Ask individual students.) Let's do it together: 1, 2, 3, 4, 5.

Listen Carefully
Number Stories

Shane was going to visit his grandmother. In his suitcase he packed his teddy bear, a box of cereal, his baseball hat, his baseball cards, and a box of crayons. How many things to wear did Shane pack? (1 thing to wear)

Shane's dog is 5 years old. His cat is 6. Which is younger? (Shane's dog)

He has had his dog for 5 years. The cat has lived with them for 4 years. Which animal has lived with them longer? (his dog)

Clap and Count

Counting

Have children listen as you slowly clap or stamp out the value of a number. Call on volunteers to say the number of claps or stamps.

A child may act as the leader.

Concept of Zero
Counting

How many windows are there in the room?

How many doors?

How many real giraffes? (0)

How many clocks are in the room? How many chalkboards? How many bookshelves? How many tables? How many live dinosaurs?

Continue with similar questions.

Describe Number Shapes
Numeration

Describe a number and have the children guess which one it is. For example: "I am thinking of a number. It looks like two circles hooked together, one on top of the other. What is it?" (the number 8)

"I'm thinking of a number. It has one straight line going down and another straight line at the top. What is it?" (the number 7)

After a few examples, let a child try to describe a number for the class.

"Body Sound" Counting

Counting

Count using sounds produced with various body parts:

> 1, 2 clap
> 3, 4 leg slap
> 5, 6 foot stamp
> 7, 8 head knock
> 9, 10 chest pound

Different Types
Number Stories

Noah asked the children at his table to name their favorite color. The answers were red, blue, pink, green, blue. How many different colors were named? (4 different colors)

Michael's mom likes to swim laps. She swims the crawl, backstroke, and side stroke. How many different ways does she swim? (3 ways)

Rhythmic Clapping
Counting

Clap out a rhythmic pattern. Have children listen and clap back
your pattern, individually or in unison.

Count the number of claps together.

Animal Sounds

Counting

Ask one child to use an animal sound (moo, cheep, woof, quack).
Give a number. The child makes that sound the given number of
times while the other children silently keep track. Everyone can say
the number at the end.

Horses
Number Stories

Shannon collects toy horses. She had 4 horses. Her brother gave her 2 more. How many horses does she have now? (6 horses)

She also owns some books about horses. She got 3 more books for her birthday. Now how many horse books does Shannon have? (Can't tell)

"Noodle Knocks"
Counting

Count and do 9 "Noodle Knocks" with me. (Knock on your head with your knuckles.)

Count and do 11 "Knee Knocks" with me.

Repeat with different numbers and types of "knocks."

"Simon Says"
Counting

Simon says: Tap your nose 10 times.
Nod your head 7 times.
Shrug your shoulders 6 times.

Repeat with different numbers and movements.

More Clap and Count

Numeration

Have children clap or stamp out the value of a number you show to them (as a group or individually).

Tap Your Tummy
Counting

Tap your tummy and count with me to 6 (or 10, or any number).

Counting Backward
Counting

Let's count backward. We'll start with 10 and go back to 0. Do it with me. 10, 9, 8, 7, . . .

You can point to a number line to help the children.

Chipmunks and Cookies
Number Stories

Seven baby chipmunks were playing beside a tree. Two went back inside the hole at the bottom of the tree. How many are playing beside the tree now? (5 chipmunks)

Karen had 2 cookies. Her brother gave her 2 more cookies. How many cookies does Karen have now? (4 cookies)

When children respond, remind them to say what the numbers describe (chipmunks, cookies, and so on.)

Countdown

Counting

Use the "Countdown" chant (10, 9, 8, 7, 6, 5, 4, 3, 2, 1, 0, BLAST OFF) at appropriate transitions.

Missing Number
Counting

Count very slowly and leave out one number. Ask: Which number have I left out?

> 1, 2, 4, 5, 6. (3)
> 7, 6, 4, 3, 2. (5)
> 10, 8, 7, 6. (9)

If the children are having difficulty, help them by saying:

> 1, 2, blank, 4, 5, 6.
> 7, 6, blank, 4, 3, 2.

Show and Tell
Number Stories

Some children brought their favorite stuffed animals for Show and Tell. Lily brought a large, brown bear. Lon brought his Snoopy dog. Tiffany brought a pink cat. Matt brought a small, light brown bear.

How many stuffed animals came to Show and Tell? (4 stuffed animals)
How many bears came to Show and Tell? (2 bears)
How many boys brought bears? (1 boy)
How many children brought animals? (4 children)

What Number Comes After? (10–21)
Counting

Have the children give the number that comes after 7, after 3, after 8, and so on. This can lead into counting from 10 to 21: What comes after 10? After 11? After 12? ... After 20? Then count from 10 to 21.

After practicing counting forward from 10 to 21, help the children count backward from 10 to 0.

Compare Body Heights to Objects
Measurement

Call on children to estimate where their heights come on taller objects or where the heights of shorter objects come on them.

More Than...
Counting

Name any number more than 10. Now give the number that comes next.

Repeat, using different numbers and giving as many children a turn as possible.

Treats

Number Stories

Andrew, Edith, John, Lucie, and Susan ate oranges for lunch. How many girls ate oranges for lunch? (3 girls)

Carlos wanted some iced tea. He put three ice cubes in a glass and poured the hot tea over them. What happened to his tea? What happened to the ice cubes?

(Remember to use the children's names when telling number stories.)

Count and Tap
Counting

Have children form a circle. Walk around the circle, counting out loud slowly. At several points tap a child and have that child give the next number.

In the Yard
Number Stories

How many animals did José see? He saw 1 squirrel, 2 chipmunks, and a sandbox in the back yard. How many animals is that? (3 animals)

There were 5 acorns. The squirrel took 4 of them. How many did he leave behind? (1 acorn)

Clap and Count Clues
Counting

Direct one child to clap or stamp out the value of a number shown only to him or her. The rest of the group counts silently and then says the number aloud.

Comparing Ages
Number Stories

Danielle is older than David. David is older than Sarah.
Who is older, Danielle or Sarah? (Danielle)

Sarah is 3 years old. David is 2 years older.
How old is David? (5 years old)

Danielle is 6 years old. David is 5 years old.
How much older is Danielle? (1 year older)

Foot-tap Counting

Counting

Tap your foot and count with me to 10 (to 17, to 21, and so on).
Tap one time for each number.

Ages
Time

How old are you?

How old will you be next year?

How old were you last year?

How old will you be in 3 years?

Finger Math Combinations
Operations

Have children hold up the correct number of fingers as you say:
Show me 4 with one hand.
Show me 4 with two hands.

Next, hold up fingers and have children mirror you and count the fingers. Use fingers on one hand or on both hands, making different finger combinations for the same number. For example:
7: 3 fingers and 4 fingers, 2 fingers and 5 fingers
3: 3 fingers on one hand, 2 fingers and 1 finger

Say the Next Number
Counting

Begin counting from 1. Stop counting and point to a child who then says the next number in sequence. Continue counting and stop again.

Repeat the process, stopping at different numbers.

Shapes in the Room

Geometry

Call on children to name 3 shapes in the room that are squares
(circles, triangles, rectangles).

Nod Your Head

Counting

Nod your head and count with me to 7 (or 12, 17, 21, and so on). Nod one time for each number.

Let's Count—Forward and Backward
Counting

Let's count to: 7 beginning at 1.
                     8 but we'll begin at 2.
                     9 but we'll begin at 3.
                     8 but we'll begin at 5.

Now listen carefully:
Let's count to 3 but we'll begin at 8.
Let's count to 1 but we'll begin at 9.

Family Math
Number Stories

Lamont's baby sister weighed 7 pounds. Kim's baby brother weighed 1 pound less. How much did Kim's baby brother weigh? (6 pounds)

Jeff has 3 sisters. He has 2 brothers. Which does he have more of, sisters or brothers? (sisters)

Does his family have more girl children or more boy children? (The same, counting Jeff!)

Show a Card
Numeration

Show a card with a number on it and ask what comes next. Ask if anyone knows how to write that number.

Repeat with new numbers.

More Count and Tap

Counting

While the class is waiting in line, go down the line, counting out loud slowly. At several points tap a child and have the child give the next number.

Melting to Zero
Number Stories

Janine had 2 popsicles on a hot summer day. She left them outside on a table and forgot them when her friend came over to play. How many popsicles did she have left when she went back to get them? (zero, or none)

Find the Next Number—Teens
Counting

When you count, what number comes after 12? After 15? After 17? After 11?

When you count, what number follows 13? Follows 16? What number comes after 19? After 14? After 10? After 18?

Block Towers

Number Stories

Roberto and Tami were playing in the block corner. The blocks were all different sizes and shapes. Roberto built a tower with 4 blocks. Tami built a tower with 6 blocks.

Whose tower was taller? (Can't tell. It would depend on the type of block. You might encourage children to experiment later with their own blocks.)

Guessing Numbers Drawn on Back
Numeration

Trace a number on a child's back. Have the child guess the number.

If some children need added practice in "feeling" numbers, identify the numbers as you trace them.

Counting On
Counting

Let's count to: 12 but we'll start at 5.
  15 starting at 6.
  21 starting at 9.
  9 starting at 3.

Let's count to 21, starting with 0.

The Number Before
Counting

What is the number before 12?
What is the number before 11?
What is the number before 10?

Let's count backward together from 12: 12, 11, 10, . . .

Counting and Clapping
Counting

Clap and count with me to 5 (or 10, 15, 20, 25, and so on).

Comparing Shapes
Geometry

How is a window like a book?

How is a penny like the (round) clock?

How is a book like a table?

How is a door like a chalkboard?

Encourage children to notice and describe properties that are similar, as well as those that differ between objects.

Numbers Before and After
Counting

When you count, what number follows 3? 15? 12? 8?

When you count, what number comes after 7? 11? 9? 10?

When you count, what number comes before 3? 5? 8? 6?

About How Many Children?
Estimating

About how many girls are here today? More than 10? Less than 10?

About how many boys? Let's count and check!

Which Is Greater? Which Is Less?
Numeration

Which number is greater, 3 or 5? 7 or 4? 1 or 2? 2 or 10?
Have children explain their answers. (For example, 5 is greater
than 3 because when you count, you get to 5 after you've already
counted 3.)

Which number is less, 3 or 5? 6 or 8? 9 or 10?

Expressions of Time
Time

Expressions such as *before* and *after, early* and *late, yesterday* and *tomorrow, next year* and *last year* are often confused by young children. Be alert to those having difficulty with these and other terms that describe time periods.

Ask the children:
When do you come to school? (in the morning)
When do you eat lunch? (at noon)
When do most people sleep? (at night)
When will you come back to school? (tomorrow; Monday)
When did we take our walk? (yesterday)
What is the coldest time of year? (winter)
When do things outside begin to get green? (spring)

Give Numbers Greater and Less Than
Numeration

Give a number greater than 3.
Give another number greater than 3, and another, and so on.

Give a number that is less than 5.
Give another number less than 5, and so on.

1 More

Number Stories

Jo has 2 dolls. Cheryl has 1 more doll than Jo has. How many dolls does Cheryl have? (3 dolls)

My tomato plant had 7 tomatoes on it. It grew 1 more tomato. Then how many tomatoes were there? (8 tomatoes)

Lunch Time Geometry

Geometry

Have the students look for shapes in their lunches. (lunchbox, sandwich, thermos, fruit, milk carton, and so on)

See if they can change any of the shapes by nibbling (for example, biting a rectangular sandwich into a triangle).

"I Spy a Shape"
Geometry

Choose an object and say "I spy a square (circle, triangle, rectangle)."

Give clues as necessary. ("It's in this half of the room.
It's near the ceiling.") The children try to guess your object.

When they are familiar with the game, let children choose the
shapes and give the clues.

Part 2

The following activities, along with previous Minute Math activities, reinforce the Ongoing Daily Routines and the activities through Section 6 in the Teacher's Guide to Activities. Remember that any Minute Math activity can be used with appropriate changes as often as you like throughout the year.

NOTES

Standing in Line
Counting

Call several children to stand in a line at the front of the class. How many children are standing in line? Who is standing first, third, fourth, and so on?

Finger Addition
Operations

Hold up 2 fingers on one hand and 3 fingers on the other.
Bring your hands together. How many fingers all together?

Do several problems, each time starting with simple combinations
and increasing as children gain mastery.

Guess My Number

Numeration

Say, "I'm thinking of a number less than 21," and let children take turns guessing what it is. Tell them when they are getting "hotter" or "colder."

Repeat with other numbers. Use a number line if needed.

Joining and Giving Away
Number Stories

David has 3 toy cars. Therese has 4 toy cars. How many toy cars do both children have altogether? (7 toy cars)

If you have 2 crayons and you give your neighbor 1 crayon, how many crayons will you have left? (1 crayon)

Eduardo had 9 cents. Then he earned 1 cent more. How many cents does Eduardo have now? (10 cents)

Leaving Out Numbers
Counting

I will count and leave out one number. Tell me what number it is.

0, 1, 3, 4, 5. (2)
12, 13, 14, 16. (15)
21, 22, 24, 25. (23)

Draw Numbers in the Air
Numeration

Call out different numbers and have the children use large arm motions to draw the numbers in the air.

Let's Count—20s and 30s
Counting

Let's count to: 26 starting at 16.
                      31 starting at 25.
                      35 starting at 21.

Let's count to 35.

Greater Than and Less Than
Numeration

Give a number greater than 13.
Give another number greater than 13, and another, and so on.

Give two numbers that are less than 15.
Give another number less than 15.

Counting Down

Counting

Give the numbers in order from 4 to 2; 3 to 1; 7 to 5; 6 to 4; 9 to 7; 5 to 3; 10 to 8; and so on.

Spending Pennies
Number Stories

Sara went to the store with 4 pennies to buy candy. She dropped 2 pennies into a mud puddle and couldn't find them. How many pennies did she have left? (2 pennies)

If each piece of candy costs 1 penny, how many pieces can she buy? (2 pieces)

Counting Backward—What Is Missing?
Counting

I'm going to count backward from 7: 7, 6, 5, 3, 2, 1. Did I leave out any numbers?

How would you count backward from 7? (Ask individual students.)

Let's do it together: 7, 6, 5, 4, 3, 2, 1.

Ordering a Line
Counting

While waiting in line ask: Who is first in line?
Second from the end?
Third from the beginning?
In the middle?

What Comes After and Before?
Counting

Count the three numbers that come after 9; after 15; after 19; after 28; and so on.

Counting backward, give the three numbers that come before 5; before 8; before 10; and so on.

(Use a number line if necessary.)

Taller, Farther, Longer
Number Stories

I live in a 6-story building. My friend lives across the street in an 8-story building. Whose building is taller? (my friend's)

Chan ran 3 laps around the track. Josh ran 2 laps. Who ran farther? (Chan)

Adam and Ariel have new sleds. Adam's sled is 3 feet long and Ariel's is 4 feet long. Whose sled is longer? (Ariel's) How much longer is Ariel's sled? (1 foot longer)

Which Is Heavier?

Measurement

Which is heavier: a mouse or an elephant? A bike or a car?
An apartment building or a dog house?

Which is lighter: a feather or a brick? A party balloon or
a basketball? An oak tree or a tulip?

Name a Number

Counting

Name any number less than 20. Now give the number that comes next. (Do this with several numbers.)

Name another number less than 20. Now give the number that comes *before* that number. (Do this with several numbers.)

Tell a Number Story
Number Stories

Tell us a 3 story (a story that has 3 as the answer).

Tell us a 0 story.

Tell us a 2 story.

Counting 10s
Counting

Let's count the fingers in our room by 10s.
Have each child hold up the fingers of both hands and put them
down as they are touched and counted: 10, 20, 30, . . .

Mark the 10s on your Class Number Line for easy counting of 10s.

Numbers on the Board
Counting

Write the numbers 3, 4, 5, 6, 7, 8, 9 on the board.

Ask: If 3 is first, what is 4? (second) 7? (fifth) 9? (last or seventh)
If 9 is first and 3 is last, what is 8? 5? 4?

Check to be sure the children know which number is the "first" one
before asking for the second, third, and so on.

Birthday Party
Number Stories

Roberto had a birthday party. His friends Kim, Ted, and Tomi were there. His mother and grandfather were both at the party. How many people were at the party? (6 people) How many children were at the party? (4 children)
(Repeat the story if necessary.)

Each child had a birthday hat. How many birthday hats were there? (4 hats)

How old was Roberto on his birthday? (Can't tell from the story)

(Remember to use the children's names.)

Say the Next Numbers—1 to 50
Counting

Begin counting from different numbers. Stop counting and point to a child, who then says the next 3 or 4 numbers in sequence. Stop that child (with a hand signal or stop sign) and point to another child, who keeps counting. Continue counting and stopping until you reach 50.

Repeat the process, stopping at different numbers.

Fall Leaves

Number Stories

Maria and Jack found colored leaves under the trees in the park. Maria took home 8. Jack didn't take home that many. How many leaves did Maria take home? (8 leaves) How many leaves did Jack take home? (We don't know—just that it was less than 8.)

More Let's Count

Counting

Let's count to: 22 starting at 15.
                           33 starting at 27.
                           42 starting at 35.
                           50 starting at 43.

Let's count to 50 starting at 0.

Here's a Riddle
Numeration

I'm thinking of a number. It's greater than 1. It's greater than 4.
It's less than 6. What number is it? (5)

Make up similar riddles for other numbers. Let the children try to
make up some.

Give Any 3 Numbers
Counting

Tell me any 3 numbers that are less than 12.
Tell me any 3 numbers that are greater than 12.

Name all the numbers between 30 and 37; 14 and 18; 45
and 49; and so on.

(Encourage children to use a number line if needed.)

Birthday Card
Number Stories

Anna's grandmother had a birthday on November 13. (Use any recent date.)

Anna mailed her a card 3 days before her birthday. On what date did she mail it? (November 10)

It took her card 3 days to be delivered. On what date was it delivered? (November 13) (Use a calendar to help children.)

Days of the Week
Time

What day of the week is it today?

What day was it yesterday?

What day will it be tomorrow?

What day will it be after that?

First or Last?
Counting

Draw a row of stick pictures on the board (or on tag board for repeated use).

Ask "Which figure is at the beginning of the row? At the end?" Then have the children tell which picture is first, third, sixth, and so on.

Finger Math
Operations

Hold up some fingers on one hand. Ask how many.

Hold up some fingers on the other hand. Again, ask how many.

Bring the hands close together. Ask: How many fingers are there all together?

Repeat using other finger combinations.

Greater and Less
Numeration

Tell me a number greater than 30.
Tell me another number greater than 30, and another, and so on.

Give two numbers less than 25.
Give another number less than 25.

(Children may want to refer to a number line.)

At the Zoo
Number Stories

At the zoo, Sandra saw one snake that was 4 feet long, a second snake that was 2 feet long, and a third snake that was as long as the first and second snake together. How long was the third snake? (6 feet long)

Sherry had 6 pennies. She bought a monkey eraser for 2 pennies. Does Sherry have less money now? (yes) How much money does Sherry have now? (4 cents, or 4 pennies)

Measuring Tools
Measurement

What would you use to measure the temperature, a bathroom scale or a thermometer?

What would you use to see how tall you are, a measuring tape or a bathroom scale?

What would you use to find out how much you weigh, a bathroom scale or a yardstick?

Numbers Before, After, and Between
Counting

Give the two numbers that come after 23; after 35; after 49; before 16; and so on.

Give all the numbers from 33 to 39; 12 to 18; 7 to 3; 12 to 1.

Get Yourselves in Order
Counting

Ask the children to raise their hands. Then have them count off as you point to them at random. As they give the next (sequential) number they put down their hands. Tell children to remember their numbers.

When all children have received numbers (and all hands are down) ask them to silently line up in numerical order.

"I'm Thinking of a Shape"
Geometry

Think of a shape and describe its characteristics. Then have children try to guess the shape. For example: "I'm thinking of a shape that has 3 sides. What is its name?" (triangle)

When children are familiar with the game, they can think of the shapes and give the clues.

More Tell a Number Story
Number Stories

Tell us a 6 story (a story that has 6 as the answer).

Tell us a 1 story.

Tell us a 5 story.

Using "Equals"
Operations

Write a row of numbers on the board: 1, 2, 3, 4, 5, 6, 7, 8, 9, 10.
Point to numbers, saying, "Give the number that comes 2 numbers
after this one; 3 numbers after this one; 1 number before this one;
and so on."

As children respond, paraphrase what is happening by using the
terms *makes, is,* and *equals* interchangeably. For example:
6 and 2 more makes 8; 3 and 3 more equals 6; 1 less than 5 is 4.

What Number Comes Between?
Counting

What number comes between 2 and 4? 11 and 13? 34 and 36? 48 and 50?

What numbers come between 13 and 17? 21 and 24? 40 and 46?

Erasing Blackboards

Number Stories

Eddy's teacher asked Gerald, Charles, and Kate to erase the blackboards.

How many children were asked to erase the boards? (3 children)
How many girls were asked? (1 girl)

Remind children to say units (children, girls) with the numbers in their responses.

3 Numbers Before and After
Counting

Count the 3 numbers that come after 12; after 26; after 30; after 47; and so on.

Counting backward, give the 3 numbers that come before 4; before 6; before 10; and so on.

More What Number Comes Between?
Counting

What number comes between 12 and 14? 11 and 13? 14 and 16? 18 and 20?

What numbers come between 13 and 17? 21 and 24? 40 and 46?

Reading the Class Graphs
Graphing

Display graphs made previously in the classroom. Use them for dozens of *Minute Math* activities by asking the children to answer questions about the graphs.

For example, using the Birthday Graph, ask, "How many of us have birthdays in May? Which month has the most birthdays?"

Fish
Number Stories

Donna's aquarium has 3 angelfish and 2 catfish. Can we tell how many fish are in her aquarium? (yes) How many? (5 fish)

Her friend just gave her 2 goldfish. Now how many fish are in her aquarium? (7 fish)

Greater or Less

Numeration

Is 2 greater or less than 6? Is 14 greater or less than 19? Is 54 less or greater than 55? Is 23 less or greater than 28?

Is it true that 42 is less than 43? Is it true that 33 is less than 35? Is it true that 27 is less than 22? Is it true that 50 is greater than 48? Is it true that 51 is greater than 55?

Let's all count to 55.

Measuring
Number Stories

The children were measuring things at home and at school. Myra found that her back door is 3 feet wide. The door to her room is 2 feet wide. How much narrower is the door to Myra's room? (1 foot)

Philip found that the distance from his classroom to the gym is 50 feet and the distance from his classroom to the computer room is 58 feet. Which is nearer to Philip's classroom, the gym or the computer room? (the gym)

Find Plus, Minus, Equals
Operations

9 plus 1 makes how much? (10)

Do you know what 10 plus 2 equals? (12)

What is 7 minus 2? (5)

More Standing in Line
Counting

Choose several children to stand in a line in front of the class. The class counts how many children are standing in line. Ask: Who is standing first? Second? Last? Fifth?

(This is a good activity to do when you are waiting in line!)

Numbers That Come Before
Counting

When you count, what number comes before 13? 15? 18? 16? 20? 11? 17? 10?

About How Many?

Estimating

About how many chairs are there in our classroom? More than 10? Less than 10? More than 50? More than 100?

About how many tables?

Fast, Slow, First, Last
Time

Which is the fastest way to get to school: take the bus, walk, ride a bike, or ride in a car? (Answers may vary.)

Which do you do first: eat lunch or go to bed? Get dressed or go home from school?

Which do you do last: wake up or come to school? Go to bed or eat dinner?

What Number Comes Before?

Counting

When you count, what number comes before 20? Before 14?
Before 16? What number comes before 10? Before 13? Before 15?
Before 21? Before 29?

Lunch Time
Number Stories

It was lunch time. Tom had 7 carrot sticks. Carla had 5. How many more did Tom have? (2 more carrot sticks)

Rex ate 10 blueberries. Then he ate 2 more. How many blueberries did he eat in all? (12 blueberries)

Fred had several cookies. After sharing 3 of his cookies, he had 2 cookies left. How many cookies did he have at the start? (5 cookies)

(Children enjoy having their names used in the number stories.)

More Name a Number

Counting

Name any number less than 30. Now give the number that comes next. (Do this with several numbers.)

Name any number between 30 and 40. Now give the number that comes next. (Do this with several numbers.)

Share a Number Story
Number Stories

Share an 8 story with us.

Share a 4 story with us.

Share a 9 story with us.

Give Numbers After and Between
Counting

Give the 2 numbers, in order, that come after 13; after 25; after 50; after 67; and so on.

Give all the numbers from 13 to 19; 42 to 48; 17 to 13; 19 to 10.

Ferris Wheel
Number Stories

There were 8 people on a ferris wheel. After the first ride, several people felt sick and got off, but 3 people stayed on for another ride. How many people got off? (5 people)

On the next ride, some more people got on. How many people were on the ferris wheel then? (We don't know.)

Count by 10s
Counting

Let's count by 10s to 100.
(10, 20, 30, 40, 50, 60, 70, 80, 90, 100)

Numbers After and Before
Counting

Count the 3 numbers that come after 14; after 37; after 51; after 65; and so on.

Counting backward, give the 3 numbers that come before 15; before 18; before 10; before 20; and so on.

More Numbers After and Before
Counting

Count the 3 numbers that come after 37; after 62; after 49; and so on.

Counting backward, give the 3 numbers that come before 14; before 11; before 20; and so on.

(Do with or without a number line.)

Kittens

Number Stories

The Garcías have a family of 7 cats: a mother, a father, and their kittens. How many kittens are there? (5 kittens)

Brenda gave away 3 of the 5 kittens. How many kittens did she keep? (2 kittens)

More Finger Addition
Operations

Everyone hold up 3 fingers on one hand.

Now hold up 2 fingers on the other hand.

Bring the hands together.

How many fingers are up?

Comparing Numbers

Numeration

Which number is greater, 13 or 15? 17 or 14? 61 or 62? 52 or 50? 40 or 30? 23 or 33? 6 or 16?

Which number is less, 13 or 15? 16 or 18? 29 or 19? 10 or 20? 40 or 14? 12 or 20?

Counting Down—Teens

Counting

Give the numbers, in order, from 14 to 12; 13 to 10; 17 to 15; 16 to 14; 19 to 17; 15 to 13; 18 to 14; 20 to 10; and so on.

(Use a number line if necessary.)

Give Numbers in Order
Counting

Give the numbers, in order, from 61 to 67; 52 to 58; 63 to 69; 55 to 58; 18 to 13; 19 to 11; and so on.

Let's all count to 70 together.

Ordinal, Standing in Line
Counting

When they are in line, ask the children to "count off" and to remember their numbers. Then ask: Who is ninth? Thirteenth? Fourth? Seventh? Twenty-first?

Give the Next Number
Counting

When you count, what number comes after 75? After 82?
After 58? After 33? After 50?

When you count, what number follows 64? 72? 81? 47? 13?

Count by 5s
Counting

Practice counting by 5s using the children's hands. "Each hand has
5 fingers. Let's count by 5s to see how many fingers are in the room."
Have the children hold up both hands and put each one down as it is
touched and counted. Lead the class: 5, 10, 15, 20, 25, 30, 35, 40, . . .

Mark the 5s on your Class Number Line for easy counting by 5s.

Cleaning Up
Number Stories

Joe, Rebecca, and Chad were cleaning up the block corner. Joe put away the long rectangles, Rebecca put away the squares, and Chad put away all the rest. The long rectangles were the first to be put away. Rebecca was finished before Chad. Who finished first? (Joe) Who finished second? (Rebecca) Who finished third? (Chad)

Why didn't they finish at the same time? (Number of blocks they had to pick up, speed at which they worked, weight of the blocks, and so on)

Name Any 3 Numbers
Counting

Name any 3 numbers less than 55.
Name any 3 numbers greater than 55.

Name all the numbers between 3 and 7; 13 and 17; 23 and 27; and so on.

(Children may find it helpful to use a number line.)

Counting by 5s
Counting

Let's count to 50 by 5s: 5, 10, 15, 20, . . .

(Emphasize the chant while counting.)

3 Numbers That Follow
Counting

Count the 3 numbers that follow 76; 44; 88; and so on.

Counting backward, give the 3 numbers that come before 7; 19; 23; and so on.

Counting Between Numbers
Counting

Count from 14 to 18; 27 to 32; 61 to 67; 88 to 90; 40 to 46; 47 to 51; and so on.

Count from 38 to 34; 20 to 16; 14 to 10.

On the Playground
Number Stories

Three girls were on the playground, playing with some boys. There was 1 more boy than there were girls. How many boys were there? (4 boys) How many children were there altogether? (7 children)

The 7 children were playing. Then 1 child left to go inside. Then 2 more children went inside.

How many children went inside? (3 children)
How many children were left outside? (4 children)

Julie has 6 mosquito bites and Yoshi has 3. How many bites do they have all together? (9 bites)

Money Comparisons
Number Stories

Debbie and Greg are both selling lemonade. Debbie charges 5 cents for a cup. Greg charges a nickel and a penny for the same size cup. From whom would you buy a cup of lemonade? Why?

Name 5 Numbers

Counting

Name 5 numbers that are greater than 27 and less than 33, but are not the same number.

Name 5 numbers that are greater than 52 and less than 58, but are not the same number.

How Many More? How Many Left?
Number Stories

One day, 5 crates of chocolate milk and 3 crates of white milk were delivered to the school lunchroom. Did they bring more crates of chocolate milk or more crates of white milk? (chocolate milk) How many more? (2 crates)

Today, 4 children have Show and Tell. Already 3 of them have had their turns. How many children still need a turn? (1 student)

Counting Up and Back
Counting

Count the numbers from 34 to 38; 57 to 62; 20 to 15; 86 to 90; 14 to 10; 58 to 63; and so on.

Count from 16 to 9; 38 to 46; 77 to 81.

How Many More?

Number Stories

A shirt has 6 buttons. It needs 9 buttons. How many more buttons does it need? (3 more buttons) (Have the children count on from 6 to 9.)

There are 8 hot dogs in a package. How many more hot dogs does it take to make 10? (2 more hot dogs) (Have the children count on from 8 to 10.)

Penny Facts

Money

Tell me something about a penny. (Worth 1 cent, has a picture of Lincoln, copper-colored, and so on)

"I'm Thinking of a Number"
Numeration

Say, "I'm thinking of a number that is 1 less than 20." Have the children guess the number. Use any numbers and clues. (Encourage children to use a number line if needed.)

Think of a Number Story
Number Stories

Think of a 10 story.

Think of a 0 story.

Think of a 7 story.

(Call on children to tell their stories.)

Pets
Number Stories

Toshi has 2 cats, 3 rabbits, and 1 bird. How many animals does she have? (6 animals)

Toshi gave the 3 rabbits to her class as classroom pets. How many animals does she have now? (3 animals)

The class has 3 rabbits. How many more rabbits do they need if they want to have 5 rabbits altogether? (2 more rabbits)

About How Many Do You Think?
Estimating

About how many children here have brown hair? How many do you think? About how many have blond hair? Is your estimate closer to 10 or closer to 100? Why?

About how many children do you think are wearing blue?

(After the children have had an opportunity to make and explain their guesses, count to verify.)

Which Number Is Smallest?
Counting

Tell me which number is the smallest.
27, 26, 25, 24, 23.

Here's another string. Tell me which number is the smallest.
22, 23, 24, 25, 26.

This time I'm going to be tricky. Listen closely and tell me which number is the smallest. 27, 22, 26.

(Begin with 3 mixed numbers and increase as children catch on.)

How Many Pieces?
Number Stories

David had 12 pieces of licorice. His sister, Abby, had 10. Who had more pieces of licorice, David or Abby? (David) How many more pieces did he have? (2 pieces)

The two children were given 6 balloons to share equally. How many should each child have? (3 balloons)

Tell Any 3 Numbers
Counting

Tell any 3 numbers less than 80.
Tell any 3 numbers greater than 80.

Let's start at 50 and count to 80 by ones.

(Children may find it helpful to use a number line.)

"I'm Thinking of a Coin" (Penny)

Money

I'm thinking of a coin. It has a picture of Abraham Lincoln on one side. The Lincoln Memorial is on the other side. It's the color of copper. It's worth 1 cent. What is it?

(Add one clue at a time until a child guesses the answer.)

Sharing Pennies
Number Stories

Eric and Robby are best friends. One day Eric brought 4 pennies to school and Robby brought 5. Robby wanted his friend to have as many pennies as he had, so he gave Eric 1 of his. Did they both have the same number of pennies then? (no) Why not? (Have two children act this out.)

Find Numbers Before, After, and Between
Counting

Give the numbers on both sides of 55; 81; 20; 63; 19; and so on.

What numbers come between 56 and 64? Between 73 and 68? Between 37 and 42? Between 79 and 82?

How Many Pencils?

Number Stories

Nate was asked to sharpen 5 pencils. Luis was asked to sharpen 3 pencils. Which boy sharpened more pencils? (Nate) How many more? (2 more pencils)

Johanna can find only 2 of her 5 pencils. She must hunt for the missing pencils. How many pencils must she hunt for? (3 pencils)

Lori has 2 blue pencils and 5 yellow pencils. How many pencils does Lori have? (7 pencils) How many more yellow pencils than blue ones does Lori have? (3 more yellow pencils)

How Many Days?
Time

How many days are in a week? (7 days)

How many days are in the weekend? (2 days) Which days are they?

How many days per week do we usually come to school? (5 days)
Which days are they?

Give Numbers After and Before
Counting

When you count, what is the number that comes after 65? After 89? After 19?

Name any number that comes before 31; before 74; before 51; before 60.

Dime Facts

Money

Tell me something about a dime. (worth 10 cents, smaller in size than a penny, picture of Roosevelt, picture of a torch between olive and oak branches, and so on)

Apple Math
Number Stories

Jeffrey brought a box of apples to school. It weighed 8 pounds. The box by itself weighed 1 pound. How much did the apples weigh? (7 pounds)

There were apple slices for snacks that day. Yoshi, Alix, and Joan sat at a table together. They were given 6 apple slices. If the 3 girls shared the apple slices equally, how many did each girl eat? (2 slices) (You may want the children to act this out.)

(Remember to use children's names in the stories.)

What Comes Next?

Counting

I'll say the first number. You say what comes next. 9; 16; 23; 37; 44; 52; 65; 78; 81; 89.

Use different numbers to help the children learn the number sequence between 1 and 90.

Walking to School
Number Stories

Martin walks 4 blocks to school and 4 blocks home each day. How many blocks does he walk to and from school in a day? (8 blocks)

On his way to school, Martin noticed that the thermometer outside the school read 25 degrees. On his way home it read 35 degrees. How many degrees did the temperature rise? (10 degrees)

Say Numbers Before, After, and Between
Counting

Say the numbers on both sides of 23; 41; 60; 20; 12; and so on.

What numbers come between 28 and 32? Between 47 and 51?
Between 82 and 87? Between 29 and 31?

Half

Number Stories

Ann has 10 stuffed animals. She shares half of them with Fred. How many stuffed animals does Fred have? (5 stuffed animals)

Tomi has 6 marbles. He shares half of them with Ellen. How many marbles does Ellen have? (3 marbles)

(Remember to use the children's names in number stories.)

More Leaving Out Numbers
Counting

I will say some numbers and leave out one number.
Tell me which number I forgot.

> 51, 52, 54, 55 (53)
> 36, 38, 39, 40 (37)

I will give a string of numbers and mix up two of the numbers.
Tell me which two numbers I mixed up.

> 68, 69, 70, 72, 71 (72 and 71)
> 21, 20, 22, 23, 24 (21 and 20)

Counting Shoes by 2s
Counting

Let's count how many shoes are at our meeting. A quick way to count them is to count by 2s.

Have the children stick out their feet. Count off by 2s.

Say Any 3 Numbers
Counting

Say any 3 numbers that are less than 85. Say any 3 numbers that are greater than 85.

Let's count from 55 to 85.

(Children may find it helpful to use a number line.)

3-Step Problems
Number Stories

Ken had 2 marbles. He won 2 more and then lost 3. How many marbles did he end up with? (1 marble)

Nomi's dog had 6 puppies. Then 2 puppies ran away, but later 1 was found. How many puppies does Nomi have now? (5 puppies)

Compare Areas

Measurement

Point to two rectangular objects that are obviously different in size (chalkboard and desk; book and window). Ask which would take more paper to cover.

(Anyone who has doubts can check it out later.)

Find Numbers Between

Counting

Name 5 numbers that are greater than 38 and less than 44, but are not the same number.

Name 5 numbers that are greater than 64 and less than 70, but are not the same number.

Keeping Track of Time

Time

What are some things in the room that help us keep track of time? (clock, kitchen timer, teacher's watch) Anything else? (calendar for days, weeks, months, year; daily schedule for days; and so on)

How Much Money?
Number Stories

A soccer ball costs $9. It costs $1 more than a football. How much does the football cost? ($8)

Eli was given $5 for his birthday. He found that the soccer ball was on sale for $6. How much more money does he need? ($1)

His uncle gave Eli $1. Does he have enough money to buy a soccer ball now? (yes)

More Numbers That Follow
Counting

Count the 3 numbers that follow 45; 57; 78; and so on.

Counting backward, name the 3 numbers that come before 13; 7; 30; and so on.

Let's all count to 90 together.

How Many All Together?
Number Stories

Maurice has 3 yellow pencils, 4 purple ones, and 1 blue one. How many pencils does he have in all? (8 pencils)

In a pet show there are 3 dogs, 5 cats, and 1 hamster. How many pets are there in all? (9 pets)

Counting On Using Fingers
Operations

Hold up 2 fingers of one hand. Say, "2." Count the remaining fingers of that hand as you raise them. (3, 4, 5)

How many fingers did we count the first time? (2) How many fingers did we count next? (3) How many fingers did we count altogether? (5)

Nickel Facts

Money

Tell me something about a nickel. (Worth 5 cents, picture of Thomas Jefferson, picture of Monticello, bigger than a dime in size, silver or gray, and so on)

How Many Cents?
Number Stories

Amir has a dime. Alex has 10 pennies. Does one boy have more money than the other? (No, a dime is worth 10 pennies.) Alex gave 1 of his pennies to Amir. Now who has more money? (Amir) How much money does he have? (11 cents, or 1 dime and 1 penny) How much money does Alex have? (9 cents, or 9 pennies)

The Flea Market
Number Stories

Room K-2 was having a Flea Market. Most of the children brought 1 or 2 old toys to sell.

Emmy brought some cars. They sold for 5 cents each. Saul bought 2 of them. How much did he pay? (10 cents)

Tami sold her blocks for 5 cents each and her stickers for a penny each. Jean bought 1 block and 2 stickers. How much did she pay? (7 cents)

Dan sold his tennis balls for 5 cents each. Emmy bought 4. How much did she pay? (20 cents)

continued

Matt had a dime. How many tennis balls could he buy from Dan? (2 tennis balls)

Matt decided to buy only 1 ball. What did Dan need to give him in exchange for his dime? (a tennis ball and 5 cents, either as a nickel or as 5 pennies)

Alison wanted 2 tennis balls. She had a nickel and a penny. Was that enough? (no) How many balls could she buy? (1 ball) How much money would she have left over? (1 penny or 1 cent)

When the sale was over, the children counted the money they had made. It came to 5 dollars and 50 cents. What do you think they should buy for the class?

Name Numbers in Order
Counting

Name the numbers, in order, from 34 to 38; 57 to 62; 14 to 9; 95 to 100; 4 to 0; 58 to 63; and so on.

Pennies and Nickels
Number Stories

Linda has a nickel. Her friend Richard has 5 pennies. Linda says she has more money than Richard. Is that true? (no)

A whistle costs 5 cents. Can Linda buy it? (yes)
Can Richard buy it? (yes)

Let's Count Nickels
Money

Let's count how many nickels are in 50 cents. (Use real or play nickels as you count.) 5 cents, 10 cents, 15 cents, ... 50 cents.

(After reaching 50 cents, count the number of nickels.)

Can I Buy It?
Number Stories

Gina and Paul were counting their pennies. Gina has 7 pennies. She wants to buy a 10-cent ball. How many more pennies does she need? (3 more pennies)

Paul has 5 cents. He would like to buy a magnet that costs a dime. How much more money does he need? (5 cents, 5 pennies, or a nickel more)

(Use the children's names in number stories.)

Think of Any 3 Numbers
Counting

Think of any 3 numbers less than 90. Think of any 3 numbers greater than 90.

Let's count by 10s past 90.

(Children may find it helpful to use a number line.)

Number Stories to Fit Equations
Operations

Tell us a 2 + 3 story.

Tell us a 5 − 1 story.

Tell us a 4 + 2 story.

(Provide examples, if needed.)

Quarter Facts
Money

Tell me something about a quarter. (Worth 25 cents, larger than a nickel, picture of Washington on one side, silver or gray, and so on)

Equivalences and Straws
Operations

A girl had 4 straws in her 2 hands. How many straws could she have in this hand (right) and in this hand (left)? (3 and 1, 2 and 2, 4 and 0) Could there be other ways to arrange them?

Repeat with other numbers of straws.

How Long? How Tall?
Number Stories

Hannah's hair is 15 inches long. It is 1 inch longer than Tammy's hair. How long is Tammy's hair? (14 inches)

Maria's desk fits under the window sill in her room. The window sill is 34 inches high. How tall is her desk? (less than 34 inches)

Which Is Longer?
Time

Which is longer, an hour or a minute?

Which is longer, a day or an hour?

Which is longer, an hour or a half-hour?

Which is longer, a half-hour or a minute?

Listen carefully: a minute, a half-hour, an hour, a day. Are these in order from the shortest to the longest? (yes)

Water Volume
Number Stories

Karlis measured 2 cups of water and poured it into a pot. The pot was then half full. How much water does it take to fill the pot? (4 cups)

He dropped a large rock in the pot. What do you think happened to the water level? (It rose.)

(Children enjoy hearing their names in the number stories.)

7 Nickels
Counting

How many cents do I have if I have 7 nickels? Let's count by 5s to find out.

5 cents, 10 cents, 15 cents, . . . 35 cents. (Use real or play nickels as you count.)

Money Exchange with Pennies
Money

To make an even trade, how many pennies must I give for a nickel? (5 pennies) A dime? (10 pennies)

How many nickels must I give for a dime? (2 nickels)

Which Coins?
Number Stories

Sam had 6 cents. Which coins could he have that make 6 cents?
(6 pennies, or 1 nickel and 1 penny)

Monique had a dime. She bought a piece of candy for 5 cents. Which
coins could she get back as change? (1 nickel, or 5 pennies)

Part 3

The following activities, along with previous
Minute Math activities, reinforce the Ongoing
Daily Routines and the activities through Section
8 in the Teacher's Guide to Activities. Remember
that any Minute Math activity can be used with
appropriate changes as often as you like
throughout the year.

NOTES

Tell Numbers After and Before
Counting

When you count, what number comes after 25? After 69? After 99?

Tell me any number that comes before 51; before 44; before 11; before 90.

Temperature Change
Number Stories

How much does the temperature rise when it goes from 70 degrees to 76 degrees? (6 degrees) (Demonstrate degrees on a thermometer.)

The thermometer read 55 degrees at noon. It was 10 degrees colder at night. What did the thermometer read then? (45 degrees) (Again, demonstrate with thermometer.)

How Far? How Much?
Number Stories

Martha walked 6 blocks to school, and Leslie walked 3 blocks less than Martha. How many blocks did Leslie walk? (3 blocks)

The rug in Kendall's room is 8 feet wide. It is 2 feet longer than it is wide. How long is his rug? (10 feet)

Jason weighs 42 pounds. Glen weighs 1 pound less than Jason. How much does Glen weigh? (41 pounds)

What Number Follows?
Counting

When you count, what number comes after 75? After 86? After 52?

When you count, what number follows 23? 16? 47? 64? 99?

Plus, Minus, Equals
Operations

How much is 5 minus 3? (2)

What does 2 plus 4 equal? (6)

What does 7 plus 2 make? (9)

"I'm Thinking of a Coin" (Dime)
Money

I'm thinking of a coin. It's the smallest coin in size, but not in value. It's the color of silver. Franklin D. Roosevelt's picture is on one side. There is a torch between two branches on the other side. The coin is worth 10 cents. What is it?

(Add one clue at a time until a child guesses the answer.)

Value of 6 Dimes

Money

How many cents do I have if I have 6 dimes? Let's count by 10s to find out. 10 cents, 20 cents, 30 cents . . . 60 cents.

(Use 6 real or play dimes as you count.)

Pennies and Dimes
Number Stories

Mari has 2 dimes and Lisa has 20 pennies. Mari wants to trade her dimes for Lisa's 20 pennies. Is that fair? (Yes. Two dimes have the same value as 20 pennies.)

Lisa lost 1 of her pennies. How many pennies does she have now? (19 pennies) Do you think that Mari still wants to make a trade? (No)

How Many Dimes?

Money

How many dimes do I need to make 1 dollar? We can count by 10s to 100 to find out. 10 cents, 20 cents, 30 cents, . . . 90 cents, 100 cents, or 1 dollar.

(Use real or play dimes as you count. When you reach 1 dollar, count the number of dimes it took.)

Which Takes Longer?

Measurement

Which will take longer to sweep, the classroom floor or the hallway? Why do you think so?

Name Numbers Before, After, and Between
Counting

Name the numbers on both sides of 15; 28; 50; 73; 99; and so on.

What numbers come between 56 and 64? Between 13 and 8? Between 37 and 42? Between 89 and 92?

I Spy Shapes
Geometry

Play "I Spy" with shape clues. Also include other attributes.

"I spy a brown square."

"I spy a large blue rectangle."

"I spy a sphere with black and white hexagons on it."

"I'm Thinking of a Coin" (Nickel)

Money

I'm thinking of a coin. It is larger than a dime in size, but not in value.
It's the color of silver. On one side is a picture of Thomas Jefferson.
The coin is worth 5 cents. What is it?

(Add one clue at a time until a child guesses the answer.)

Lunch Math
Number Stories

In her lunch box, Tori has 4 carrot sticks and 3 celery sticks. She has as many cookies as vegetable sticks. How many cookies does she have? (7 cookies)

Tom had 4 cookies in his lunch and ate 3 of them. Then he gave 1 cookie to Jonathan. How many cookies does Tom have left? (0 cookies, or none)

Stickers
Number Stories

Monica is collecting stickers. They cost 10 cents each. She has
8 pennies in her piggy bank. How many more pennies does she need
to buy a sticker? (2 more pennies)

Her grandmother gave her enough nickels for 1 sticker. How many
nickels did she give her? (2 nickels)

Her big sister gave her enough dimes for 1 sticker. How many dimes
did she give her? (1 dime)

Bake Sale
Number Stories

May had 5 cents. She spent 4 cents at the bake sale. Her mother gave her another 2 cents. How much money does May have now? (3 cents)

Mario had a dime. He bought some peanuts for a nickel. How much money does he have left? (5 cents, 5 pennies, or a nickel)

When he went home, his father gave him 5 cents. How much does Mario have now? (10 cents) Does he have more, less, or the same amount as he had to begin with? (the same) (Reread if necessary.)

"I'm Thinking of a Coin" (Quarter)

Money

I'm thinking of a coin. It's the largest one we've studied, both in size and in value. It's the color of silver. On one side is a picture of George Washington. The coin is worth 25 cents. What is it?

(Add one clue at a time until a child guesses the answer.)

More Plus, Minus, Equals
Operations

What does 3 plus 3 equal? (6)

What does 8 minus 2 equal? (6)

How much is 4 plus 5? (9)

Five and Dime Store

Number Stories

Tami wants 3 kites. They cost 10 cents each. How much must she pay? (30 cents) (Count by 10s.)

How many 10-cent stickers can Connie buy for 40 cents? (4 stickers) (Count by 10s.)

At 5 cents each, how much will 9 pencils cost? (45 cents) (Count by 5s.)

Money Exchange with Quarters
Money

How many quarters must I trade for 1 dollar? (4 quarters)

Which Is Longer?
Time

Which is longer, an hour or a minute?

Which is longer, a day or an hour?

Which is longer, a day or a week?

Which is longer, a week or a year?

Clue Counting to 100

Counting

Have the children repeat after you: 9, 10, 11; 19, 20, 21; 29, 30, 31; 39, 40, 41; 49, 50, —; 59, 60, —; . . . 99, 100, 101. Explain that this is a way to help them count to 100.

Practice at odd moments.

As a variation, go around the circle, with each child supplying the missing number.

What Time? (To the Hour)
Time

Show 8:00 on a demonstration clock. Ask: What time is it?

Show 3:00. What time is it?

Show 10:00. What time is it?

Show 12:00. What time is it?

Switching Numbers
Counting

I will name some numbers in a string. I will switch 2 of the numbers around. Which numbers are switched?

24, 25, 27, 26, 28, 29. (27 and 26)
20, 19, 17, 18, 16, 15. (17 and 18)
4, 5, 7, 6, 8. (7 and 6)
9, 7, 8, 6, 5. (7 and 8)

At the Park
Number Stories

Two boys raced down the hill. Adam got to the bottom in 30 seconds,
but Ariel arrived in 20 seconds. Who got to the bottom first? (Ariel)
How long did Ariel wait for Adam? (10 seconds)

One pitcher contained 4 cups of lemonade and another contained
3 cups. How many cups of lemonade were there in all? (7 cups)

People drank 5 cups of lemonade at lunch. How many cups of
lemonade were left? (2 cups)

Money Exchange

Money

To make an even trade, what coin must you give me for
5 pennies? (nickel) 10 pennies? (dime) 25 pennies? (quarter)

To make an even trade, what must you give me for 100 pennies?
(dollar bill, 10 dimes, and so on)

Spending Money
Number Stories

Kathy has 15 cents. She earns 10 more cents. How many cents does she have now? (25 cents) Does she have more or less than she started with? (more)

Ken buys a 25-cent stamp. He pays 30 cents. How many cents does he get back in change? (5 cents)

Terri has 14 cents. She spends 1 cent. How many cents does she have now? (13 cents)

Skip Counting

Counting

Begin counting by 2s, 5s, or 10s. Stop counting and point to a child, who then says the next numbers in sequence. Stop the child with a signal (a stop sign or raising your hand) and point to another child, who continues counting.

Keep counting and stopping until you reach the desired number. Repeat the process, stopping at different numbers.

How Many Kinds?

Number Stories

A piggy bank contains 5 pennies, 2 nickels, 1 dime, and 1 quarter. How many different kinds of coins are in it? (4 different kinds)

A mother hen has 7 chicks, and 5 of these chicks are black. The others are yellow. How many chicks are yellow? (2 chicks)

Hour Hand

Time

What hand on the clock tells you the hour? (the short hand)

Where is the short hand pointing on our classroom clock? What hour is it closest to?

Find Numbers After and Before
Counting

When you count, what is the number that comes after 42? After 76? After 23? After 100?

Tell me any number that comes before 56; before 68; before 37; before 90; before 100.

Months and Seasons
Time

What month is this?

What season is this?

What was last month?

What will it be next month?

What will it be the month after that?

What will the next season be?

Comparing Numbers

Number Stories

If Terrence took 10 books and put them into 2 even piles, how many books would be in each pile? (5 books)

Mia and Jason shared 6 cookies. Mia ate 1 and Jason ate 5.
How else could they have shared the cookies? (2 and 4, 3 and 3, 4 and 2, 5 and 1, 6 and 0, 0 and 6)

What Do You Add or Subtract?
Operations

What do you subtract from 8 to get 8? (0)

What do you add to 1 to get 5? (4)

What do you subtract 1 from to get 6? (7)

What do you subtract 2 from to get 6? (8)

How Many Left?
Number Stories

The children saw 8 penguins on the rock at the zoo. Soon 4 large penguins and 3 baby penguins slid back into the water. How many of the penguins were left on the rock? (1 penguin)

Yoshi folded 2 origami bunny rabbits and 2 origami ducks. She gave 3 origami animals to Tina. How many did she have left? (1 animal)

Learning Hours

Time

Use a paper clock with only the hour hand. Set it and ask the class "About what time is it?" Reset it and ask again.

How Much Do You Add or Subtract?
Operations

How much do you add to 6 to get 8? (2)

How much do you subtract from 8 to get 7? (1)

How much do you add to 4 to get 6? (2)

What Number Comes After? (High Numbers)
Counting

When you count, what number comes after 75? After 102? After 58? After 33? After 50?

When you count, what number follows 64? 72? 101? 47? 13?

The Hour Hand

Time

Look at the clock. What number is the hour hand nearest to now?
About what time do you think it is?

Magician Tricks
Number Stories

Jan's uncle is a magician. He put a scarf in his big top hat. Jan reached in and found 2 scarves. Then the magician put 2 rubber balls in his hat. Jan reached in and found 3 rubber balls. If the magician puts 4 candy bars in his hat, how many do you think Jan will find there? (5 candy bars)

What happens each time Jan reaches into the hat? (Jan finds 1 more thing has been added.)

Left or Right?

Counting

Quickly write several numbers in a line on the board. Ask which is the left side and which is the right side. Then tell the children:

Read the third number from the left.
Read the first number from the right.
Read the fourth number from the right.
Read the second number from the left.
Read all of the numbers from left to right.

Show the Hour

Time

Show 6:00 on a demonstration clock and ask what time it is. (Stress that the short hand tells the hour.)

Show 7:00 on the clock. What time is it?

Show 2:00. What time is it?

Show 11:00. What time is it?

Show 12:00. What time is it?

Number Stories Using Food

Number Stories

There are 10 cookies in a box. Half of the cookies are chocolate. How many are chocolate? (5 cookies)

Four children bought a box of candy. There were 8 pieces in the box. They shared the candy equally. How many pieces did each child take? (2 pieces)

(Allow children to act out the stories, as needed.)

Counting On—3 Numbers
Counting

Counting on, name the 3 numbers that follow 76; 44; 88; and so on.

Name any 3 numbers that come before 27; 80; 66; and so on.

Missing Addends
Number Stories

Aaron is 6 years old. Bruce is 3 years older. How old is Bruce?
(9 years old)

Bruce and Aaron went to the rodeo Saturday. They saw 7 white horses and 3 black horses. How many more white horses did they see than black horses? (4 more white horses) How many horses did they see all together? (10 horses)

The Minute Hand

Time

What hand on the clock tells you the minutes? (the long hand)

Where does the minute hand point when the time is exactly at the hour? (straight up, or at 12)

What Do I Have to Do?
Operations

I have 5. I want 7. What do I have to do? (Add 2)

I have 6. I want 3. What do I have to do? (Subtract 3)

I have 10. I want 8. What do I have to do? (Subtract 2)

Buying with 10 Cents
Number Stories

Nick wants to buy a 10-cent ticket. He has only 7 cents. He needs how many more cents? (3 cents) (Count on to find out.)

If you have 10 cents and spend it all on 2 balls that cost the same amount, what does each ball cost? (5 cents)

More Find the Numbers Between
Counting

Name 5 numbers that are greater than 58 and less than 64, but are not the same number.

Name 5 numbers that are greater than 84 and less than 90, but are not the same number.

The Hands of the Clock
Time

What hand on the clock tells you the minute? What hand on the clock tells you the hour?

Ask the following questions only on the hour:

Where is the long hand pointing on our classroom clock? (straight up or at the number 12)

Where is the short hand pointing? What hour is it pointing to?

What time does our clock say?

How Many More Do I Need?
Operations

I have 5 cookies. I need 8 cookies for my party. How many more cookies do I need? (3 cookies) (Have the children count on from 5 to 8 and keep track with their fingers if needed.)

I have 9 eggs. How many more do I need to make a dozen? (3 eggs) (Be sure the children know that a dozen means 12. Have them count on from 9 to 12.)

Money Exchange Using Dimes
Money

How many dimes must I trade for a dollar? (10 dimes)

How many dimes must I trade for 2 dollars? (20 dimes)

(Count by 10s using real or play dimes.)

Just Before Lunch
Time

How long do you think it will take us to wash and line up for lunch?
Okay, let's do it and see.

Which Takes Longer?
Number Stories

Sparrow eggs hatch in 3 weeks. Penguin eggs hatch in 8 weeks.
Which eggs take longer to hatch? (Penguin eggs) How much longer?
(5 weeks longer)

How Many Dollars?

Money

How many dollars must I trade for a 10-dollar bill? (10 dollars)

How many dollars must I trade for a 100-dollar bill? (100 dollars)

Money Exchange with Dollar Bills
Money

How many ten-dollar bills can I get if I have 14 one-dollar bills?
(1 ten-dollar bill) Will I have any one-dollar bills left? (yes) How
many? (4 one-dollar bills)

If I have a dollar and I find a quarter, how much money do I have?
(a dollar and a quarter, or 1 dollar and 25 cents)

90 to 115
Counting

Give the numbers on both sides of 100; 110; 114; and so on.

Let's all count from 90 to 115 together.

More Number Stories to Fit Equations
Operations

Tell us a 9 + 1 story.

Tell us a 9 − 1 story.

Tell us an 8 + 2 story.

Which Is Faster?

Time

Do you think it would be faster to crawl across the room or walk across the room? Why?

If we count with a medium, steady beat, do you think it will take closer to 10 counts, 50 counts, or 100 counts to walk across the room? Let's try!

Fairy Tales
Number Stories

Jack wondered how high his beanstalk grew. If you were Jack, how would you measure it?

If the Mama Bear from The Three Bears story has 2 more baby bears, how many kids will be in the Bear Family? (3 kids) How many bears will be in the family? (5 bears) Can you think of a number sentence to show the total number of bears in the family?

How many bricks do you think the third little pig used to make his house? Less than 10? More than 10? More than 50? More than 100? Much more than 100? Why do you think so?